FOLENS IDEAS BANK RE CHRISTIANITY

Elaine McCreery

Contents

Folens Publishers

How to use this book

Ideas Bank books provide you with ready to use, practical photocopiable activity pages for children **plus** a wealth of ideas for extension and development.

TEACHER IDEAS PAGE　　　　　　　**PHOTOCOPIABLE ACTIVITY PAGE**

Clear focus to the activity.

Background information and other help given.

Ways of introducing the subject matter to the children.

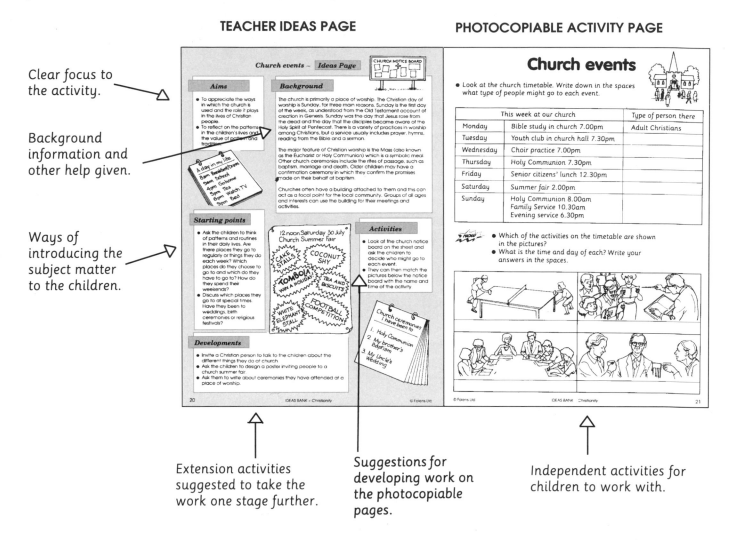

Extension activities suggested to take the work one stage further.

Suggestions for developing work on the photocopiable pages.

Independent activities for children to work with.

● Time-saving, relevant and practical, **Ideas Bank** books ensure that you will always have work ready at hand.

First published 1994 by Folens Limited.
United Kingdom: Folens Publishers, Apex Business Centre, Boscombe Road, Dunstable, LU5 4RL.
Email: folens@folens.com

Ireland: Folens Publishers, Greenhills Road, Tallaght, Dublin 24.
Email: info@folens.com

Poland: JUKA, ul. Renesansowa 38, Warsaw 01-905

Editor: Edward Rippeth　　　　Layout artist: Patricia Hollingsworth　　　　Illustrations: Tony Dover – Graham-Cameron Illustration
Cover: In Touch Creative Services Ltd　　　　Cover image: David Rose

Every effort has been made to contact copyright holders of material used in this book. If any have been overlooked, we will be pleased to make any necessary arrangements.

British Library Cataloguing in Publication Data. A catalogue record for this book is available from the British Library.

Elaine McCreery hereby asserts her moral rights to be identified as the author of this work in accordance with the Copyright, Designs and Patents Act 1988.

ISBN 1 85276 826-6

Introduction

Folens Ideas Bank RE Christianity is designed to help teachers introduce children to the traditions and religious aspects of Christianity. For each topic covered there is a teacher's ideas page and an activity sheet which can be photocopied for the children to use in class. The teacher's page provides information for the teachers about one aspect of Christianity. It sets out aims for the topic concerned, outlines the activity sheet and suggests ideas for starting and following up the topic. The activity page is photocopiable and is intended for the children's use in class after the topic has been introduced.

The current legal requirements for RE mean that all children should be introduced to the world's religions. Children are to develop a knowledge of the main beliefs and traditions of each religion, and be able to reflect on such learning in terms of their own beliefs and experiences. This book aims to bring these two strands together and as a result, each topic involves the children thinking about their own responses to subjects.

The topics chosen represent some of the most popular topics taught in RE in primary school. They serve as a basic introduction to Christianity upon which further study might be built. They relate closely to the Model Syllabuses published by S.C.A.A.

The teacher will need to do a small amount of preparatory work for each topic and some require the availability of a children's Bible.

Teaching about Christianity

Christianity is a diverse religion embracing many denominations and children should be made aware of this variety - including the fact that Christians come from a wide range of races, nationalities and cultures. Christians will vary the emphasis they place on different aspects of their faith, but central to Christianity is the belief that there is one God, made known most fully in the person of Jesus. Children should also be alerted to the fact that in this country there are a variety of ways in which people refer to themselves as Christian. The festivals of Christmas and Easter, for example, are celebrated by a wide range of people, not all of whom will be practising Christians in a committed sense. In this book, attention is drawn to the variety of Christian tradition and the focus is on the beliefs and practices of those who try to live their lives in and with Christ. Teachers need to take care when using the New Testament not to portray a negative impression of Judaism. The New Testament was not written to present Judaism in a positive light.

The aim of the work in this book is to present Christianity as a living world faith and it aims to promote positive and respectful attitudes in the children.

The main Christian denominations

Roman Catholic

Anglican

Free Churches - including Methodist, Baptist, United Reform

Eastern Orthodox - including Greek and Russian

Aims

- To understand the main beliefs of Christianity.
- To appreciate how these affect a person's life.
- To consider how we live our own lives.

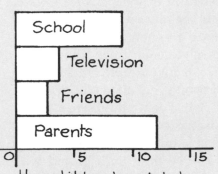

How children learn to behave

Starting points

- Ask the children how they learned how to behave - was it from from parents, school, television or friends?
- Discuss who they are friendly with and who they help - friends, neighbours or strangers.

Background

Christians believe that God created the world and that from early times God has spoken to people. They believe that God sent Jesus Christ to help bring people back to God. Jesus is believed to be God Incarnate - God in human form. They believe there is a life after death as promised by Jesus. He is believed to have come back to life after he was crucified. Christians try to follow Jesus' example and lead a good life.

The Great Commandments sum up Christian belief and can be found in the New Testament - Mark 12:30-31. In his teaching, Jesus often makes reference to Jewish laws and traditions, because he was Jewish and so were many of his audience. The Ten Commandments of Jewish law can be found in Deuteronomy 6:4-18 and Leviticus 19.

Jesus refers to the commandments in response to questions from the Jewish teachers of the law. They appear to be trying to test his understanding by asking him which is the greatest of the commandments. The teachers appear to be pleased with his response. The Jews of the time interpreted 'neighbour' as 'fellow-countryman'. Jesus uses it to refer to anyone. In one of Jesus' stories, 'The Parable of the Good Samaritan'(Luke 10:25-37), he draws attention to the question 'who is my neighbour?'. The hero of the story is a Samaritan who would normally be an enemy of the Jews. Jesus uses the story to illustrate that the way you treat your fellow humans is more important than religious ritual.

Activities

- Read the commandments and discuss their meaning.
- Talk about ways in which Christians might follow the commandments in everyday life.
- The children could work out ways of helping people who have different needs.

Developments

- Organise a fund-raising activity for a charity chosen by the children.
- Design posters to place around school which show how children can treat each other well.
- Read the story of the Good Samaritan and discuss the implications of 'loving your enemy'.

IDEAS BANK – *Christianity*

The Great Commandments

● Decorate this scroll with patterns of your own design.

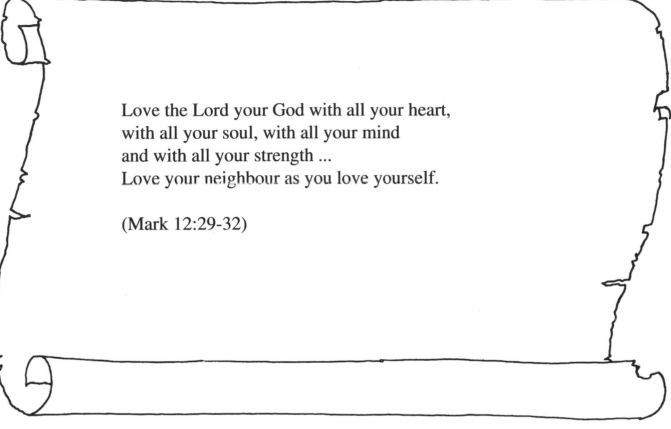

Love the Lord your God with all your heart,
with all your soul, with all your mind
and with all your strength ...
Love your neighbour as you love yourself.

(Mark 12:29-32)

 ● How could a Christian be a good neighbour to these people?
Write your answers in the spaces.

An elderly person	
Someone who is ill	
Someone they have argued with	
A homeless person	

The Lord's Prayer - Ideas Page

Aims

- To become familiar with one of the most famous Christian prayers.
- To understand some Christian beliefs as outlined in the prayer.
- To consider what is meant by prayer.

Background

Jesus' teaching on prayer reflected his Jewish background. Jews were required to pray three times a day, including praying in public. Jesus offered a new approach to prayer which differed from both Jewish and Gentile prayers. He said that prayer should be done privately rather than in public and should be short. Prayers would be answered but people should be ready to forgive others. He also stressed the importance of praying for others.

In the Lords' Prayer, Jesus used his own language rather than Hebrew, the language of the scriptures. There are two versions of the prayer, in Matthew 6:9-13 and Luke 11:2-4. However, the best-known version is in *The Book of Common Prayer,* which is used in a number of Christian churches. There are also other versions with more modern language. The word 'Father' originates from an Aramaic word 'Abba', a term a child would use. 'Hallowed be thy name', and 'thy kingdom come' originate from Jewish prayer. 'Bread' can mean physical sustenance, but may also mean 'Bread of Life' (John 6:35), a term referring to everlasting life.

Times we might pray

1. When we are sad.
2. When a friend or relative is ill.
3. When somebody is in trouble.
4. When we have done something wrong.

Starting points

- Ask the children what they know about prayer - what is it for, who does it, what do people say?
- Ask if any of them know the Lord's Prayer. Where did they learn it? When do they say it?

Bread is a symbol of life

Developments

- The children could write prayers specific to a particular situation.
- Investigate prayers from other religious traditions.
- Talk to Christian people about prayer and what it means to them.

Activities

- Read through the prayer aloud, or have the children read through quietly by themselves.
- Pick out the different sections and discuss the meaning, highlight words that are new.
- The children can then consider the questions on the sheet and illustrate the prayer if they wish.
- Other questions to consider are:
  - Why might Christians call God 'Father'?
  - What does 'Hallowed' or 'Holy' mean?
- Explain the meaning of 'Amen' (it signifies agreement).

The Lord's Prayer

● These are the words of the Lord's Prayer.

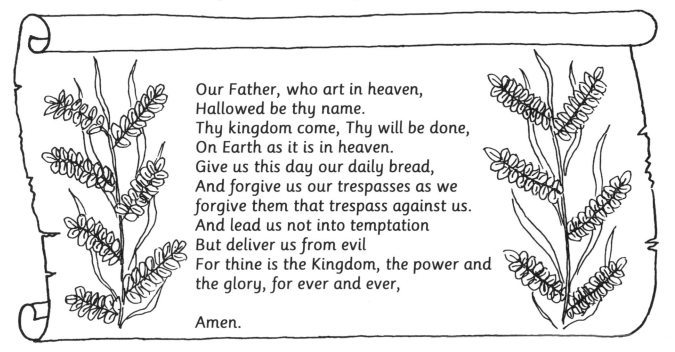

Our Father, who art in heaven,
Hallowed be thy name.
Thy kingdom come, Thy will be done,
On Earth as it is in heaven.
Give us this day our daily bread,
And forgive us our trespasses as we
forgive them that trespass against us.
And lead us not into temptation
But deliver us from evil
For thine is the Kingdom, the power and
the glory, for ever and ever,

Amen.

NOW ● In the spaces below, write the answers to the following questions:

● What do you think the kingdom of heaven might be like?

_____

_____

● What trespasses, sins or wrongdoings do people do?

_____

_____

● What temptations do you face?

_____

_____

Lifestyle – Ideas Page

Aims

- To recognise how Christians put their beliefs into action.
- To consider what influences there are on how we live our lives.

Starting points

- Collect leaflets from Christian charity groups such as Christian Aid and the Christian Children's Fund. These are available from charity shops or local churches.
- Discuss how we live our daily lives and how we know what is right.

Background

There is a great emphasis in Christianity on personal belief. A true Christian is considered to be one who has undergone baptism of his or her own accord. They have few rules or ritual obligations dictating their everyday lives. Many pray regularly and take part in their own personal devotions, often using the Bible. Prayer positions include kneeling, bowing, putting hands together and waving hands in the air, usually facing the altar when in church. Most attend some form of congregational worship and some will occasionally go on 'retreat' for spiritual refreshment.

There is a long tradition among Christians of assisting the poor and needy, based on the teachings of Jesus. Some Christians devote their lives to helping others. They may give money, both in church and at other times and some Christians may set aside an amount each week. Some believe that they have a duty to influence the way other people behave and the way society is run. They join organisations which strive to improve society in general, morality, the environment, health, social justice and human rights. Many embark on pilgrimages to special places for Christians, such as Jerusalem and Lourdes. Christian values include courage, forgiveness, peace, self-sacrifice, commitment, love and justice.

FAMOUS CHRISTIANS

MOTHER TERESA (b.1910)
She helps the starving and homeless in India.

MARTIN LUTHER KING (1929 - 1968)
He fought for equal rights for black Americans.

WILLIAM WILBERFORCE (1759 - 1833)
He campaigned for the abolition of slavery.

Activities

- The activity focuses on how Christians put their beliefs into action by helping others.
- Look at some of the leaflets and discuss who is being helped and in what ways. It may be that money is required to help others but it may also include giving one's time or other assistance.
- Discuss why Christians believe it is necessary to help others - through the teachings of Jesus and the examples of his healing ministry.
- Ask them which of the statements might apply to Christians and to suggest some of their own. They could give reasons for their answers.

Developments

- Find out about famous Christians, such as Mother Teresa, Martin Luther King and William Wilberforce.
- Ask a Christian person to talk to the children about how they put the teachings of Jesus into action.
- Use maps to find places of pilgrimage in Christian tradition.

Being a Christian

Christians try to live the way Jesus taught them.

● Tick which words show what a Christian should be like.

helpful		kind	
unfriendly		selfish	
spiteful		rude	
loving		mean	

● Tick the things a Christian should try to do.

pray		ignore people	
not share things		eat too much	
read the Bible		give to charity	
help parents		have fun	

● Have your friends ticked the same things?

 ● Make a list of other things a Christian might try to do.

_____   _____

_____   _____

_____   _____

_____   _____

_____   _____

_____   _____

Aims

- To explore the evidence in the New Testament about the life of Jesus.
- To develop knowledge of the historical figure and consider other aspects of his life.

Background

Christians believe that Jesus was the son of God and at the same time was God 'incarnate' - in the flesh. He was born as a Jew in Bethlehem about 2000 years ago, the son of Mary who was married to the carpenter Joseph. Little is known about his early life. At the age of 30 he began preaching and teaching around Palestine. The Gospels tell of Jesus' life, work and death but other references to Jesus can be found in Jewish and Roman writings of the time. Jesus came into conflict with the Jewish leaders, who passed him to the Romans for execution. Christians believe that on the third day after his death, Jesus' tomb was found empty and he appeared to various followers.

The Holy Land

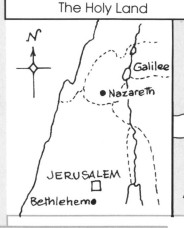

Starting point

- Discuss with the children who Jesus is and what he did. They may already know something about him from school, reading, or church. Many will think of the baby from the Christmas story, others may know of his work and death. The discussion should include a consideration of where the children got this knowledge from.

Activities

- Ask the children to complete the first part of the sheet by themselves and before any discussion. They are asked to note three things they know about Jesus.
- Before they share this with anyone they should consider how they know this information.
- Then the children can compare their thoughts with someone else and discuss where they could find out more. If there are areas of disagreement, this can be discussed.
- The information can then be shared across the class and compiled in a display.
- Conflicting information can be identified and the children can suggest how to find out which is correct.
- They will need to be reminded that some information cannot be found in a book and that they may need to ask Christians their thoughts instead.

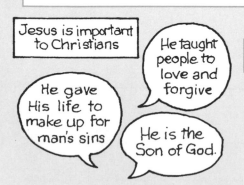

What we know about Jesus

1. He was born in a stable in Bethlehem.
2. He had 12 disciples.
3. He was crucified.
4. He healed lots of people by miracles.

Jesus is important to Christians

He taught people to love and forgive

He gave His life to make up for man's sins

He is the Son of God.

Developments

- Invite a Christian person to come and answer the children's questions about Jesus.
- For Christians, the historical detail about Jesus is only one aspect of knowing about him. Discuss with the children what it might be about Jesus that is important to Christians.

IDEAS BANK – *Christianity*

What do we know about Jesus?

● In the spaces below, write three things you know about Jesus.

● How did you know these things about him? _____

_____

Show your sheet to your neighbour. Have they got the same
information as you?

NOW ● What else would you like to find out about Jesus?

_____

_____

Aims

- To develop the children's knowledge of Jesus through the study of stories.
- To understand that Christians base their lives on an understanding of what Jesus taught.
- To reflect on their own treatment of people in their own society.

Starting points

- Read Jesus' parable of the lost sheep to the children.
- Talk about things that are precious to them. How would they feel if these things got lost.

Background

Jesus often taught in parables, which are stories with different levels of meaning. Several of his parables tell of lost things. Jesus uses them to speak of God's concern over people who have been lost to Him through sin. Jesus had a special concern for the poor and society's outcasts. According to ancient Jewish law, some people were considered unclean and outcasts in society. This could be related to their work (such as tax collectors), appearance (lepers) and religion (Gentiles or non-Jews). Such people were not considered part of ordinary society and Jews were advised not to mix with them in case they made themselves unclean. Jesus uses the parable of the lost sheep to make the contrast between righteous people and the self-righteous. He criticised the Jewish religious leaders for their self-righteousness and their lack of compassion for those they considered unclean. Jesus often used images of an agricultural life in his parables, reflecting the experiences of his audience.

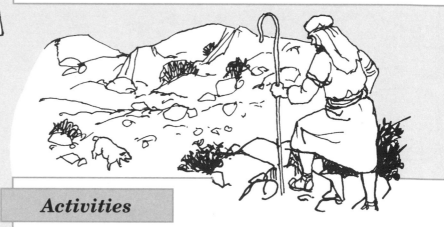

Activities

- The children may need some explanation about the setting of the story, as they may not be familiar with the life and work of shepherds. Tell them about the laws which made some people outcasts in Jesus' time.
- Read the story together and discuss the meaning.
- The children might need to underline words that are new to them for explanation.
- Discuss which people are treated as outcasts today, such as the homeless. How are they treated by the rest of us?

Developments

- Find other parables about lost things in Luke's gospel. For example Luke 15:8-10, Luke 15:11-32.
- Find other references to sheep and shepherds, such as John 10:1-8.
- Create a wall display showing Jesus' stories about lost things.

The lost sheep

● Read the following story. It is taken from Luke 15:1-7.

One day, when many tax collectors and other outcasts came to listen
to Jesus, the Pharisees and the teachers of the law started grumbling:
'This man welcomes outcasts and even eats with them!' So Jesus told
this parable.

'Suppose one of you has a hundred sheep and loses one of them -
what does he do? He leaves the other ninety-nine sheep in the pasture
and goes looking for the one that got lost until he finds it. When he
finds it, he is so happy that he puts it on his shoulders and carries it
back home. Then he calls his friends and neighbours together and says
to them, "I am so happy I found my lost sheep. Let us celebrate!"
In the same way, I tell you, there will be more joy in heaven over one
sinner who repents than over ninety-nine righteous people who do not
need to repent.'

● What message was Jesus
giving to the people?

_____

_____

_____

● Why did Jesus tell stories
about shepherds?

_____

_____

_____

● Why were the Pharisees
unhappy with Jesus?

_____

_____

_____

NOW

● Find out about these words: repent, celebrate, outcasts
and sinner.
● Find out what you can about the Pharisees, life in Jesus' time
and other stories Jesus told.

Disciples – Ideas Page

Aims

- To understand what a disciple is and learn more about Jesus' disciples.
- To consider the qualities that disciples might need in order to do their work.
- To think about what makes people change their whole life for what they believe in.

Background

The word 'disciple' means 'follower', and Jesus' disciples were mostly Galilean Jews, like himself. Jesus chose 12 disciples from a variety of backgrounds (this probably echoes the 12 tribes of Israel, as described in the Old Testament). The disciples left their work and families to follow Jesus. They joined him in his work and assumed the responsibility of spreading the Gospel (Good News) after his death. Their role was to help bring people back to God. Jesus addressed a lot of his teaching to the disciples in response to their questions. Jesus seemed to expect that the disciples would suffer as a result of following him. Sometimes the disciples appear not to understand his teaching. There are several examples of the disciples' discussion with Jesus, including Mark 1:16-20, 4:35-41, 6:45-56 and 10:35-45.

The disciples were: Simon Peter (Jesus gave him the name Peter), James and John (sons of Zebedee), Andrew (brother of Simon Peter), Philip, Bartholomew, Matthew (a tax collector), Thomas, James (son of Alphaeus), Thaddaeus (son of James), Simon the Canaanite, Judas Iscariot.

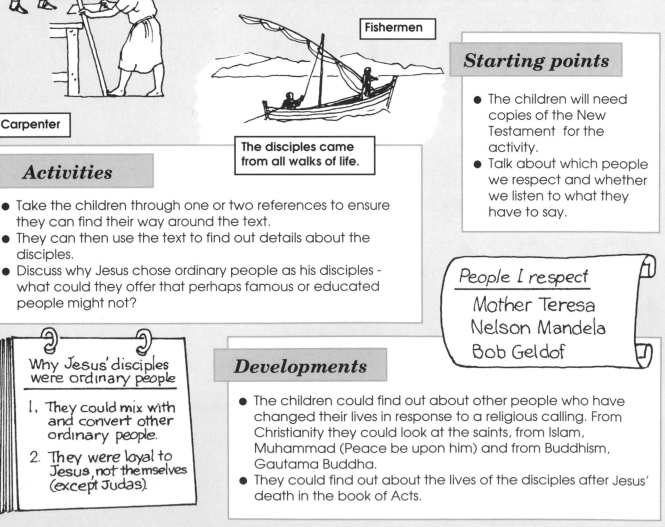

Tax collector

Carpenter

Fishermen

The disciples came from all walks of life.

Starting points

- The children will need copies of the New Testament for the activity.
- Talk about which people we respect and whether we listen to what they have to say.

Activities

- Take the children through one or two references to ensure they can find their way around the text.
- They can then use the text to find out details about the disciples.
- Discuss why Jesus chose ordinary people as his disciples - what could they offer that perhaps famous or educated people might not?

People I respect
Mother Teresa
Nelson Mandela
Bob Geldof

Why Jesus' disciples were ordinary people

1. They could mix with and convert other ordinary people.
2. They were loyal to Jesus, not themselves (except Judas).

Developments

- The children could find out about other people who have changed their lives in response to a religious calling. From Christianity they could look at the saints, from Islam, Muhammad (Peace be upon him) and from Buddhism, Gautama Buddha.
- They could find out about the lives of the disciples after Jesus' death in the book of Acts.

IDEAS BANK – *Christianity*

Followers of Jesus

- Use the Bible references to find out the answers to the following questions.
- Where did Jesus find his disciples Philip and Nathaniel?

Philip _____ John 1:44

Nathaniel _____ John 1:44

- What job did these disciples do?

Andrew _____ Mark 1:16

Matthew _____ Matthew 10:3

- Who was the father of James and John?

_____ Mark 1:19

- Which disciples are being described here?

He tried to walk on water. _____ Matthew 14:29

He was the son of Alpheus. _____ Luke 6:15

He betrayed Jesus with a kiss. _____ Matthew 26:14-15

He wanted proof that Jesus was alive. _____ John 20:25

NOW • Write a job description for a disciple. What would he or she have to do?

```
┌─────────────────────────────────────────────┐
│              DISCIPLE WANTED!                 │
│                                               │
│  _____  │
│  _____  │
│  _____  │
│  _____  │
│  _____  │
└─────────────────────────────────────────────┘
```

St Paul - Ideas Page

Aims

- To introduce the children to the figure of St Paul and his importance in Christianity.
- To consider the concept of changing one's life for the better.

Why people are hostile to other groups

1. Ignorance
2. Fear of the unknown.
3. They don't feel good about themselves

Background

Paul was a devout Jew, originally named Saul (a Hebrew/Aramaic name). He was a well-educated citizen who persecuted Christians. However, while travelling on the road to Damascus, Paul was blinded by a light and heard the voice of Jesus ask 'Why do you persecute me?' Some days after, Paul's sight was restored by a disciple called Ananias and Paul became a believer in Christ.

Paul became Christianity's greatest missionary and early theologian, taking the Gospel (good news) to Gentiles (non-Jews). He went on three missionary journeys, was imprisoned several times and eventually he was probably executed. The teaching of Paul and the early church is recorded in the New Testament in his letters to Christian communities. Paul developed much of the early church's beliefs and teaching and taught that Jesus could be called 'Christ' (anointed one). He believed that people were affected by original sin and needed to be baptised in the name of Jesus to overcome this. Jesus' self-sacrifice on the cross had atoned for people's sins. The resurrection was his triumph over sin in the world.

Starting points

- Discuss events in the children's lives when they may have changed their mind or view of things. What difference did it make?
- Discuss why some people are hostile to other groups, for example through racism.

Some of the places visited on Paul's first two journeys

Activities

- Read to the children the story of Paul's conversion (Acts 9).
- Talk about why Paul persecuted Christians (fear of the unknown, a threat to his beliefs and so on).
- The children can either produce their own pictures or use the ones on the activity sheet. They can then put the story in order.

Developments

- Read stories of Paul's life after his conversion (Acts).
- Ask the children to find the places visited by Paul on two of his missionary journeys (see above), using a modern map or globe. They could plot the routes and note any differences between Paul's time and now. Ask them to find another of Paul's journeys in Acts and plot the route.
- Ask the children to write an account of Paul's conversion from the point of view of an eyewitness.
- Find stories of other people who made big changes in their lives because they believed God wanted them to, such as Chad Vara, the founder of the Samaritans.

A change of heart

● Cut out the pictures and, using the sentences below, place them in the correct order.

1. Saul takes letters to Damascus to arrest Christians.	4. God sends a disciple of Jesus, called Ananias, who restores Saul's sight.
2. There is a blinding light and Saul falls over. He hears a voice saying, 'Saul, Saul, why do you persecute me?'	5. Saul is baptised and begins to spread the Christian message.
3. Saul is blind. He is led to Damascus and does not eat for three days.	6. Saul becomes a great missionary and makes three journeys.

Inside a church – Ideas Page

Aims

- To recognise the significant parts of the church building and the role they play in Christian worship.
- To encourage the children to use their own knowledge of churches as a basis for discussion.

Background

The word 'church' can refer to the building itself, or the world-wide community of Christians. Churches can be built in any design, traditional ones being built in the form of a cross when seen from above, recalling the crucifixion of Jesus. Some Christians may gather in someone's home to worship. The main focal point is the altar, from which Holy Communion or the Eucharist is given. The main features of the church are an indication of the activities that go on there. They will be used for regular weekly worship, festivals and for special occasions such as rites of passage (weddings, birth ceremonies and so on).

The **altar** is the focal point for the congregation. This often consists of an image of Jesus or a **crucifix** (an image of Jesus on the cross) set on a table. The table is a reminder of the last supper. (The second 'high' altar is used to administer communion.)

The **lectern** is the stand from which the Bible is read. It indicates the importance of the Bible in Christian worship.

Starting points

- Begin by collecting pictures and posters of churches. A camera could also be used to take photographs of churches in the local area.

The **pulpit** is the stand from which the sermon is read.

The **pews** are seats for the congregation.

The **font** is the basin used for baptism. This is often placed near the door because baptism represents a person being welcomed into the church.

- The children can compare information about the churches they know. They may also know of other places where Christians meet, for example cathedrals or chapels.

Activities

- Using the pictures or photographs, identify the objects on the sheet and talk about what they are used for.
- The children can then identify other objects which appear on the pictures.

Developments

- Ask the children to compare different types of churches. In what ways are they different? Are there reasons for these differences?
- Find out about the places where Christians meet, such as cathedrals, homes and chapels.
- Organise a visit to a Christian place of worship.
- Make a model of a church from boxes. Make a model of the inside as seen from above.
- Design a stained glass window showing a story from the Bible.

Inside a church

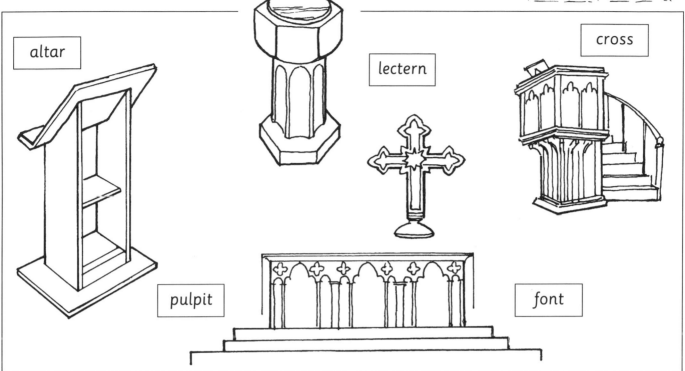

- Join these objects to their labels.
- Why are these things important in the church?

Altar _____

Cross or crucifix _____

Font _____

Pulpit _____

Lectern _____

 ● Write down what other things you might find in a church.

_____

_____

_____

_____

Church events - Ideas Page

Aims

- To appreciate the ways in which the church is used and the role it plays in the lives of Christian people.
- To reflect on the patterns in the children's lives and the value of pattern and tradition.

Background

The church is primarily a place of worship. The Christian day of worship is Sunday, for three main reasons. Sunday is the first day of the week, as understood from the Old Testament account of creation in Genesis. Sunday was the day that Jesus rose from the dead and the day that the disciples became aware of the Holy Spirit at Pentecost. There is a variety of practices in worship among Christians, but a service usually includes prayer, hymns, reading from the Bible and a sermon.

The major feature of Christian worship is the Mass (also known as the Eucharist or Holy Communion) which is a symbolic meal. Other church ceremonies include the rites of passage, such as baptism, marriage and death. Older children may have a confirmation ceremony in which they confirm the promises made on their behalf at baptism.

Churches often have a building attached to them and this can act as a focal point for the local community. Groups of all ages and interests can use the building for their meetings and activities.

Starting points

- Ask the children to think of patterns and routines in their daily lives. Are there places they go to regularly or things they do each week? Which places do they choose to go to and which do they have to go to? How do they spend their weekends?
- Discuss which places they go to at special times. Have they been to weddings, birth ceremonies or religious festivals?

Activities

- Look at the church notice board on the sheet and ask the children to decide who might go to each event.
- They can then match the pictures below the notice board with the name and time of the activity.

Developments

- Invite a Christian person to talk to the children about the different things they do at church.
- Ask the children to design a poster inviting people to a church summer fair.
- Ask them to write about ceremonies they have attended at a place of worship.

Church events

● Look at the church timetable. Write down in the spaces what type of people might go to each event.

	This week at our church	Type of person there
Monday	Bible study in church 7.00pm	Adult Christians
Tuesday	Youth club in church hall 7.30pm	
Wednesday	Choir practice 7.00pm	
Thursday	Holy Communion 7.30pm	
Friday	Senior citizens' lunch 12.30pm	
Saturday	Summer fair 2.00pm	
Sunday	Holy Communion 8.00am Family Service 10.30am Evening service 6.30pm	

● Which of the activities on the timetable are shown in the pictures?
● What is the time and day of each? Write your answers in the spaces.

The home – Ideas Page

Aims

- To appreciate the way in which the home reflects Christian commitment.
- To think of their own home as a special place.

Background

There are no particular religious duties that Christians must do in the home. Many Christians will pray in the home and some may have a small shrine (for example Roman Catholics). Orthodox families may have icons ≈ images of Jesus and the saints. Some Christian families will say grace (a brief prayer) before meals. Some have religious pictures or statues. Many Christian children are taught to say prayers before they go to sleep at night. Christians may also have a copy of the Bible and other religious writings to help them in their private worship. On Sundays, instead of working, many families spend the day together, perhaps sharing a meal.

Starting points

- Ask the children what things they do in the home. This will range from simple things, such as sleeping and eating, but they should be encouraged to think of other things, particularly those which involve sharing time with the family.
- Suggest to them that the home is also a place of security where people have a sense of belonging. Are there other places where children feel secure and safe?

Activities

- The activity focuses on prayer as an activity Christians might do in the home.
- Prayers often contain the following parts:

> **Praise for God**: Christians recognise God as creator and preserver of the world. They think of God as their spiritual father and accept their dependence upon him.
> **Thanks to God:** Christians thank God for the good things in their lives. God is provider and to him they owe their gifts and talents.
> **Asking God for forgiveness**: Christians strive to live a good life and in the manner of Jesus. They recognise that they are open to temptation. They ask God to forgive them for the things they have done wrong.
> **Asking God for help**: Christians may ask for help in their own lives if they are facing hardship. They will also pray for other people – the sick, the bereaved, the poor, asking God to comfort and support them in their need.

- Discuss with the children what kinds of things Christians might say in their prayers.
- The children can then write their own versions in the spaces.

Places where I feel secure
1. In my bed.
2. At the brownies' hut.
3. In church.
4. In my dad's car.

Developments

- Write out the children's versions of the prayers to put into a display.
- Light a candle and ask the children to sit in quietness and think of those in need.
- Invite a Christian person to talk about their own private devotions.

Praying at home

- Prayers have several different parts.
- In the spaces, write down the things that a Christian could say in each part of a prayer.

- To praise God.

_____

_____

_____

_____

- To thank God.

_____

_____

_____

_____

- To ask God for forgiveness.

_____

_____

_____

_____

- To ask God for help for themselves and others.

_____

_____

_____

_____

Amen.

Aims

- To recognise that the Old Testament is a collection of books important to Christianity.
- To understand that it is also important to Jews and to Muslims.

Old Testament books were first written on scrolls and copied by hand in Hebrew.

Background

The word 'Bible' is from the Greek word 'biblia'. Christians treat the Bible with great respect, as it represents the word of God. It is kept in a special place in the church and is a focus of attention throughout worship. The Old Testament is the first part of the Christian Bible and is a collection of books compiled over hundreds of years. The word testament means agreement or covenant. It contains 39 books and includes Jewish history, law, teaching, poetry, stories and prophecies. These were originally written in Hebrew on handwritten scrolls.

The Old Testament was used by early Christians for teaching, as they saw the life of Jesus as the fulfilment of Jewish history and prophecy. The prophets of the Old Testament spoke of a Messiah (anointed one) who Christians believe to be Jesus. The book of Matthew often refers to the Old Testament to show how prophecies had been fulfilled in the person of Jesus. Christians today still use the Old Testament for their understanding of God.

Starting points

- The children will need to refer to copies of the Bible for this activity.
- Ask them about the kinds of books they like to read.

Activities

- Using copies of the Bible, the children can then fill in the names of the books. Some are already completed to help.
- The questions at the bottom of the page could be used as an extension task encouraging children to think, or it could be discussed first.
- Show the children where different types of writing can be found in the Old Testament.

Examples of types of writing in the Bible

Type	Where found
Laws	Leviticus and Deuteronomy
History	Genesis and Exodus
Prophecy	Isaiah
Songs and poetry	Psalms

Developments

- Many Bibles contain diagrams showing how the Bible came to be in its present form today. The children could find these.
- Ask them to find some of the famous stories they know using the Bible's contents page, for example the stories of Moses, Noah and Joseph.

The Old Testament

● Look in the Bible and find the names of the books of the Old Testament.
● The first ones are done for you. Write in the other books' names.

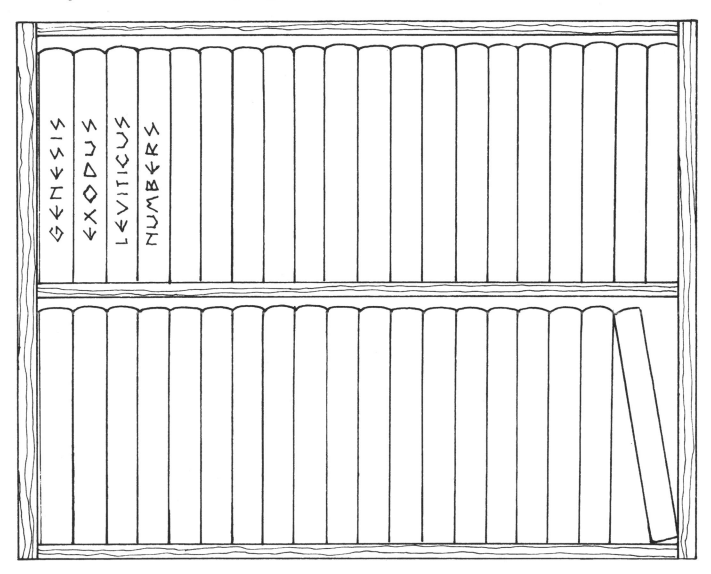

 ● What kinds of books do you like to read?

_____

_____

● Why are the books of the Old Testament special to Christians?

_____

_____

_____

IDEAS BANK – *Christianity*

New Testament – Ideas Page

Aims

- To introduce the children to the New Testament as the main scripture of Christianity.
- To understand that the New Testament is a collection of books written to spread the word about Jesus' life and death.

Starting points

- The children will need to have copies of the New Testament for reference.
- Introduce the New Testament as the main scripture of Christianity which Christians will use regularly.

Background

The New Testament is a collection of books written during the first century AD by different Christian writers. The books contain a variety of writing, including letters, but all aim to spread the word about Jesus and his life and teaching. The books were originally written in Greek, the international language of the time. Christians today use them in services and in study to learn about Jesus and what he taught.

The New Testament contains 27 books, which fall into four categories. The four Gospels (Good News) focus on the life and death of Jesus; Acts describes what happened shortly after Jesus' death; Letters (or Epistles) are written for the early churches (many by Paul); and Revelation describes the end of all things. The books are not in the order in which they were written; for example, the letters of Paul were among the earliest writings.

Books of the New Testament

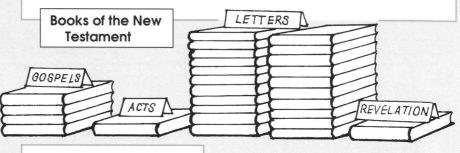

Activities

- Show the children where the New Testament can be found in the Bible, pointing out the different sections which are the various books.
- Ask them questions about the significance of the writings. Why did those who knew Jesus decide to write about him? Why did Christians keep copies of the letters? Why do Christians today still read the writings?
- The children can then try to find the names of New Testament books in the wordsearch.

Developments

- Select stories from the New Testament and read them to the children. Stories from the Gospels are particularly suitable.
- Ask the children to find out about life in New Testament times.
- Show them how Christianity spread from its earliest days in Palestine to the wider world.
- Ask them to research how the present day Bibles developed from the earliest scriptures. The Bible's history is often found in its front pages.

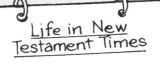

Life in New Testament Times

1. There were no cars or electricity

2. The Romans ruled a Great Empire.

3. Books could not be printed.

IDEAS BANK – *Christianity*

The New Testament

● Find the names of the New Testament books in the Wordsearch, and cross them off the list below.

C	M	A	T	T	H	E	W	G	A	L	R	1C
O	A	1P	E	T	E	R	E	A	1T	U	E	O
L	U	K	E	3J	O	H	N	L	I	R	V	R
O	M	2J	J	A	M	E	S	A	M	O	E	I
S	A	O	T	I	T	U	S	T	O	M	L	N
S	R	H	2P	E	T	E	R	I	T	A	A	T
I	K	N	J	U	D	E	J	A	H	N	T	H
A	H	E	B	R	E	W	S	N	Y	S	I	I
N	1J	O	H	N	A	C	T	S	A	C	O	A
S	O	N	P	H	I	L	E	M	O	N	N	N
1T	H	E	S	S	A	L	O	N	I	A	N	S
U	2C	O	R	I	N	T	H	I	A	N	S	A
2T	H	E	S	S	A	L	O	N	I	A	N	S

Matthew	Ephesians	Hebrews
Mark	Philippians	James
Luke	Colossians	1 Peter
John	1 Thessalonians	2 Peter
Acts	2 Thessalonians	1 John
Romans	1 Timothy	2 John
1 Corinthians	2 Timothy	3 John
2 Corinthians	Titus	Jude
Galatians	Philemon	Revelation

 ● The list contains all the New Testament books. Which four books on the list are missing from the wordsearch?

Gospels - Ideas Page

Aims

- To help the children understand that the Gospels tell the story of Jesus' work and death.
- The children will develop their research skills in locating and interpreting information.

Background

The four Gospels were written by different people at different times and for different audiences. They all tell the story of Jesus' life, work and death but their different interests mean the story varies in detail. The Gospels contain information about Jesus which show him to be the Messiah, the Son of God, Man's saviour sent by God. The most important and detailed part of each Gospel is the death and resurrection of Jesus and there is little about his early life. From reading the Gospels, Christians appreciate the personality of Jesus, who he was, what he did and said, and what happened at his death.

Starting points

- Discuss with the children what they know about Jesus and where people can find out more about him. They might suggest the Bible, a church or a Christian person.
- Remind the children that Jesus lived 2000 years ago and ask them how we find out about people who lived a long time ago, compared to finding out about people living today. Make reference to newspapers, television, diaries, biographies and so on.

The parable of the mustard seed (Matthew 13:31-32), was to explain the Kingdom of God.

Jesus' disciples go to the tomb and find it empty (John 20:1-10).

Activities

- The activity requires the children to look up and read several Bible references. From this, they can find out some of the things Gospel writers said about Jesus.
- Look up the references together and discuss what they say about Jesus.

Jesus in the cornfield gets into trouble for breaking the Sabbath laws (Luke 6:1-5).

Jesus takes his disciples to a lonely place so they can rest (Mark 6:30-34).

Developments

- The children could choose one of the references and perform the story as role-play.
- They could write an account of one of the references from the point of view of an eyewitness.
- They could use black sugar paper and coloured tissue to make stained glass windows, depicting the Gospel events.
- Ask a Christian person to come and talk to the children about how they know about Jesus. Remember that many Christians believe that it is possible to know Jesus today because of the resurrection. Learning about him through the New Testament is only one way.

Finding out about Jesus

● Check the references in the Bible. Link the story to the correct picture and reference.

Jesus tells a parable to explain about the Kingdom of God.

John 20:1-10

Jesus' disciples go to the tomb but his body is not there.

Matthew 13:31-32

Jesus gets into trouble for breaking the Sabbath laws.

Mark 6:30-34

Jesus takes the disciples to a lonely place so they can rest.

Luke 6:1-5

Baptism – Ideas Page

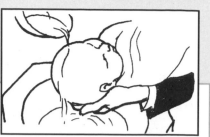

Aims

- To encourage the children to think about the way in which people are welcomed into a community.
- To learn about some of the symbolism associated with the Christian welcoming ceremony of Baptism.

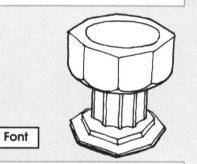

Font

Background

Baptism marks the commitment to a life following the teachings of Jesus. It originates from the work of John the Baptist, who prepared people for the coming of the Messiah. Jesus himself was baptised by John (Luke 3:1-22). Both infant and adult baptism, are practised in Christianity, although not by all Christian groups. When a child is baptised the promises of commitment are made on the child's behalf by god-parents. Water symbolises cleansing and all sins are washed away, ready for the new life.

The baptism ceremony often takes place as part of another service and is held at the font near the door of the church. The font is a large bowl-like container into which water is poured. During the ceremony the priest pours water over the baby's head, baptising him or her 'in the name of the Father and of the Son and of the Holy Spirit'. A candle is lit to signify the passing from darkness into light and as an exhortation for the child to shine as a light in the world. The baby's name will also be heard in public for the first time. In some Churches baptism involves total immersion in water, and takes place at a later age.

Starting points

- Begin with some discussion about what it means to belong to a group. What groups do we belong to, what benefits are there and what responsibilities? Are there ways in which we are welcomed to these groups?
- If possible collect pictures or photographs of Christian baptism.

The symbolism of the baptism candle.

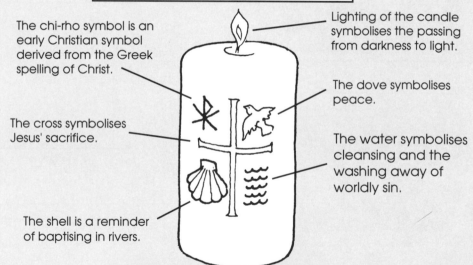

The chi-rho symbol is an early Christian symbol derived from the Greek spelling of Christ.

The cross symbolises Jesus' sacrifice.

The shell is a reminder of baptising in rivers.

Lighting of the candle symbolises the passing from darkness to light.

The dove symbolises peace.

The water symbolises cleansing and the washing away of worldly sin.

Activities

- Discuss with the children the use of water in our everyday lives. Bring out in the discussion how important water is to us and this is why it is often used as a sign of life.
- Show them pictures of a baptism if possible, or tell them briefly what it is about.
- Ask them to think about the meaning of baptism as they go through the sheet.

Developments

- The children could find out from their families if they had any welcoming ceremony when they were born.
- Organise a visit to a local church. Ask the minister to talk the children through the baptism ceremony.
- Make a wall frieze depicting the ceremony, to include all the people involved.

Baptising a baby

- We use water for a number of things. Write some of them in the spaces.

_____   _____

_____   _____

_____   _____

- Describe what is happening in this picture.

_____

_____

_____

- Why is water used to baptise the baby?

_____

- NOW • The god-parents often help to raise a baby child as a Christian. Write down how they could do this.

_____

_____

_____

Holy Communion –

Aims

- To explore the significance of the communion meal for Christians.
- To encourage the children to consider the use of food as a symbol.

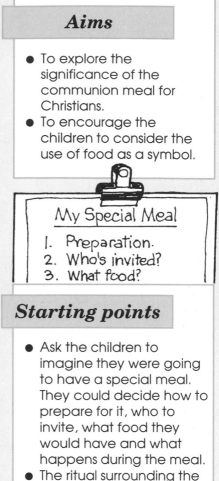

My Special Meal

1. Preparation.
2. Who's invited?
3. What food?

Starting points

- Ask the children to imagine they were going to have a special meal. They could decide how to prepare for it, who to invite, what food they would have and what happens during the meal.
- The ritual surrounding the communion meal is also seen in the way people prepare for special celebration meals. The children should recognise the importance of ritual in the Communion service.

Background

Shortly before he died, Jesus shared a final meal with his disciples (Mark 14:12-26, Luke 22:7-28, Matthew 26:17-30). During the meal he referred to the bread and wine as his body and blood. He told the disciples that he would be betrayed and that his blood would be spilt for many people.

Most Christians today remember this meal through a service which has several names: Holy Communion, Mass, The Lord's Supper and Eucharist. For many Christians it is the most important act of worship. The service varies between Christian denominations, but it serves to remind all Christians of how Jesus died to atone for their sins and to enable them to come to God. By taking part in the service, Christians think of themselves as part of one body, one community.

A Typical Communion service

A set prayer, worshippers confess their sins.
Readings from Old and New Testaments.
A sermon read or given by the priest.
Gifts of money offered at the altar.
Priest blesses the bread and wine.
Members of the congregation partake of bread and wine.
Further hymns and prayers.

Activities

- Read or tell the story of The Last Supper from the New Testament.
- Discuss what Holy Communion means to Christians - it reminds them that Jesus died on behalf of all humankind.
- What happens during Holy Communion? Collect books that describe the service, or ask a Christian to explain. Try to get accounts of the service from several different Christian denominations.
- Ask the children to complete the activity sheet, using their knowledge of the Holy Communion.

Developments

- Ask a member of the Christian faith to come in and explain to the children why Holy Communion is special.
- Ask the children what other foods they have on special occasions.
- Make a wall display about bread. Show its importance as a food, how it is made and how it is used in religious tradition. For example bread is used on the Sabbath and at Passover in Judaism.

Holy Communion

● What are Christians reminded of by wine?

_____

_____

_____

● What are Christians reminded of by bread?

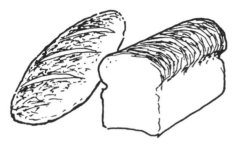

_____

_____

_____

● Write down all the names you can find for this Christian meal.

_____   _____   _____

_____   _____   _____

 ● Do you eat special food for any occasions? On the chart, write down what food you eat and when.

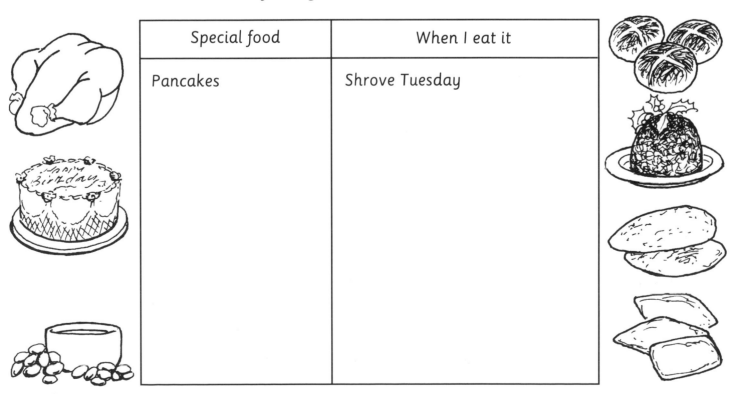

Special food	When I eat it
Pancakes	Shrove Tuesday

Marriage - Ideas Page

Aims

- To focus on the symbolism of the marriage ceremony and help the children understand the commitment that people make.
- To draw upon the children's own experiences of marriage ceremonies so they can appreciate its importance to Christian people.

Background

All Christian churches have services for marriage. It is seen as a happy event at which God is believed to be present. The marrying couple promise to live together as partners until they die. After the service, family and friends usually gather to celebrate the marriage.

Many wedding traditions have developed over the years and have little or no religious significance. Some traditions are pagan in origin. The ring is a symbol of eternity because the couple promise to marry for life. Confetti or rice is often thrown over the couple as a symbol of fertility, because everyone hopes the couple will have children. The tradition of wearing a white dress is fairly recent and symbolises purity. The bride often carries a bouquet of flowers, which symbolise life. At the wedding meal or breakfast, there is often a large cake, made in tiers, which is shared among the guests. Many couples keep the top tier to save as a christening cake for their first born child.

Starting points

- Ask the children if they have been to a wedding. Where did it take place and what happened? Was it a religious ceremony and of which tradition was it a part?
- Collect together photographs of different weddings, if possible from a variety of Christian traditions. The teacher and children could bring photos of their wedding experiences as well.

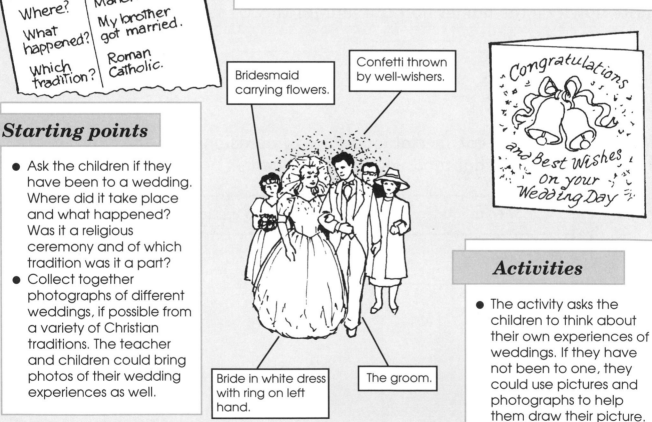

The time I went to a wedding

Where?	Manchester.
What happened?	My brother got married.
Which tradition?	Roman Catholic.

Bridesmaid carrying flowers.

Confetti thrown by well-wishers.

Bride in white dress with ring on left hand.

The groom.

Congratulations and Best Wishes on your Wedding Day

Activities

- The activity asks the children to think about their own experiences of weddings. If they have not been to one, they could use pictures and photographs to help them draw their picture.
- They then design a card to send to a couple getting married. Encourage them to include some of the traditional features they have seen and talked about.

Developments

- Act out a Christian marriage ceremony, using what the children know about such occasions.
- Invite a recently married person to tell them about their wedding and what it means to him or her.

Getting married!

- Draw a picture of a wedding.

- Design a card to send to a Christian couple who are getting married.

Death – Ideas Page

Aim

- To introduce the children to the Christian beliefs and traditions surrounding death.

Background

Christians believe, as Jesus promised, that death is not the end of existence. Fundamental to Christian belief is the concept that, through his resurrection, Jesus showed that death was not the end. He promised people that there was a life after death, where people would join him and God the Father. As a result, Christians should not mourn for long, because they can trust that the dead person is with God.

Christians hold funeral services in a church or a chapel to say goodbye. The dead person is cremated or buried. The service gives to thanks God for the life of the person and prays for his or her arrival in heaven. There are several views held about what lies in the afterlife. Flowers are usually given at funerals as a symbol of life. Those who have died are often remembered with a headstone over their grave, or a plaque at the crematorium.

How people feel when someone dies

1. Sadness
2. Great sense of loss
3. Fond memories

Starting points

- Explain to the children that many religious traditions have sets of beliefs about death and this influences the way they treat someone who has died.
- Ask the children what happens to a person once they have died. The children may have been to funerals or have seen them on television. Talk about how other people feel when someone close to them dies.

Activities

- The subject is a sensitive one and teachers will need to be aware of the personal circumstances of children before they embark on it. The need to recognise death is important in the development of children's understanding of life.
- It is not quite appropriate in the context of a classroom lesson to dwell on the practical details of dispatching a body and so instead the emphasis here is on the celebration of life in death.
- The person the children think of need not be personally known to them. They could choose a famous person whom they admire.

Developments

- Find children's stories that focus on death in a sensitive way, such as *Badger's Parting Gifts* by Sue Varley (Picture Lion). These could be used to explore some of the issues and concerns the children have about death.
- Many religious traditions have a concept of an afterlife. Ask the children what they think this might be like.

What the after life might be

1. A place above the clouds with angels and harps.
2. Re-incarnation as something else.

Remembering

Many Christians like to remember those who have died. You may know of someone who has died.

● Think of the good memories you have of them and write them on this flower.

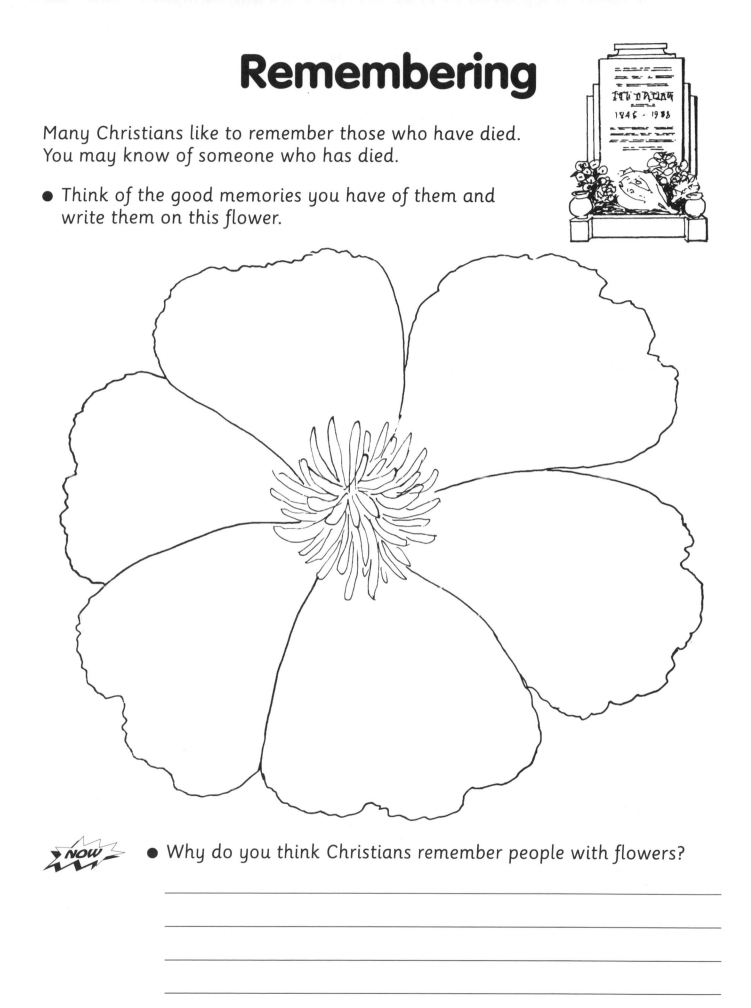

● Why do you think Christians remember people with flowers?

_____

_____

_____

_____

Advent - Ideas Page

Aims

- To develop the children's understanding of Advent and its significance for Christian people.
- To explore some of the traditions associated with it and reflect on the notion of looking forward to an event.

Background

'Advent' is from a Latin word meaning 'coming' and begins on the fourth Sunday before Christmas. It is a time of preparation for the birth of Jesus, which has been observed since about the sixth century AD. It marks the beginning of the Christian year. In church there are readings from the Bible about God's promise of a saviour, with the emphasis on preparation.

Christians often count the days to Christmas using advent calendars, rings or candles. A calendar often has pictures of the birth scene with 24 windows cut into it. It is a serious time during which Christians prepare themselves for a new beginning. In the eastern church, it is a period of repentance.

Starting point

- Begin with some discussion about looking forward to things. What events do children look forward to? What feelings do they have? How do they prepare for the event? All of these relate to the role of Advent within Christian tradition.

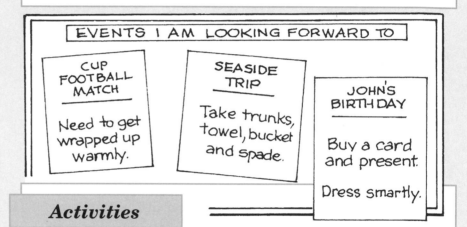

EVENTS I AM LOOKING FORWARD TO

CUP FOOTBALL MATCH
Need to get wrapped up warmly.

SEASIDE TRIP
Take trunks, towel, bucket and spade.

JOHN'S BIRTHDAY
Buy a card and present.
Dress smartly.

Activities

- Tell the children how Christians prepare for Christmas. On the one hand they will be buying presents and special food, but they will also be thinking about the coming of Jesus. What feelings might Christian people have at this time?
- Remind the children that Advent is a serious time. Talk about the things that Jesus was concerned about - the poor, the sick and the needy (see Mark 3:1-5).
- The children can draw a picture in each Advent candle to show what Christians are thinking of.

Developments

- Make an Advent crown or wreath with four candles to light during each week of Advent.
- Make Advent calendars with 24 windows. The children can open one each day to show an aspect of Advent or Christmas.
- Buy an Advent candle and set aside some time each day to burn a section. During this time the children could be encouraged to think of those people who are in need.

Preparing for Jesus

● In each candle, draw a picture to show what Christians might be thinking of during Advent.

Christmas - Ideas Page

Aims

- To help the children understand the significance of the festival to Christian people.
- To recognise the importance of the event in relation to the incarnation.
- To appreciate the use of symbolism in religious tradition.

Background

This is probably the most well-known Christian festival, but it is not the most important. Some Christian groups place very little emphasis on it. The festival recalls the birth of Jesus and stories about his birth are read and acted out. It is celebrated on 25 December, the day of an ancient pagan festival, because the exact date of Jesus' birth is not known.

Christians mark the beginning of their calendar from the date of Jesus' birth, and the years since are referred to as AD (Anno Domini, which means 'in the year of our Lord') or CE (the 'common era'). The festival is celebrated by special church services, containing particular readings and songs called carols. At home, Christians will have a celebration meal and exchange gifts. Homes are often decorated with evergreens and bright colours. Themes linked with Christmas start with the notion of the incarnation, but also include love, family and caring for the poor and needy.

Starting points

- Discuss with the children what they know about the Christmas festival. Many of them will be more aware of Santa Claus and the material side of Christmas than the spiritual aspects.
- Ask them what they know about their own birth, for example where and when.
- Talk about what gifts people bring on the birth of a baby. These may be purely practical items, such as clothing, but they could also be commemorative, like bracelets or silverware.

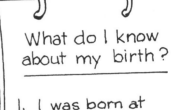

What do I know about my birth?

1. I was born at Hexham Hospital.
2. The time was 3.15 p.m.
3. I weighed 8 pounds.

Activities

- Use a children's Bible to tell the story of Jesus' birth. These versions are often a combination of the different accounts in the Gospels (see Matthew 1-2 and Luke 1-2).
- After reading the story, the children could attempt to complete the certificate. If they get stuck, they could share information.
- The gifts given to Jesus by the wise men were symbolic, foretelling his future life. Ask the children what gifts they could give to a baby to wish him or her well in the future.

Merry Christmas

Developments

- Design a Christmas card illustrating Jesus' birth.
- Perform a Nativity play.
- Design and make a crib scene.
- Tell the story of Jesus' birth from the point of view of one of the wise men.
- Compare the birth stories in Matthew and Luke.

The birth of a special baby

● When babies are born today, a birth certificate is filled in.
What would Jesus' certificate have looked like?

Name _____

Date of birth _____

Place of birth _____

Name of mother _____

Name of father _____

Occupation of mother _____

Occupation of father _____

Home country of parents _____

Witnesses _____

● The wise men brought gifts for the baby.

Representing KINGSHIP	Representing WORSHIP	Representing SUFFERING
Gold	Frankincense	Myrrh

● What special gift would you bring a baby and why?

I would bring _____

because _____

_____

Lent - Ideas Page

Aim

- To consider the importance of Lent to Christians. Emphasis is placed on the concept of self-sacrifice, which is a central theme of the period.

Starting points

- Read to the children the account of Jesus' temptations in the wilderness from a children's Bible (see Luke 4).
- Talk about the concept of preparation for an important task or event. Ask the children how they prepare for important work? How do they focus their minds on something important?

Background

Lent marks the four weeks leading up to Easter. It recalls the 40 days Jesus spent in the wilderness preparing for his ministry (Mark 1:12-13). It is a time of preparation when Christians may give up some luxuries in order to focus on their spiritual life. In the past it was a time of fasting when rich food was given up. The period begins with Shrove Tuesday, when people used to eat all of their rich food and went to church to be 'shriven' or forgiven their sins. Lent starts on Ash Wednesday, when many Christians go to church and have ash made from the previous year's palm crosses marked on their foreheads. Mothering Sunday marks a break from fasting halfway through Lent, when girls in service used to go home and visit their mothers. Today, Lent is a time for appreciating what one has in one's life and giving to other people.

The Temptations of Jesus in the Wilderness

Jesus was famished and the devil told him to turn stones into bread, to show he was the son of God. Jesus refused, saying, 'Man cannot live on bread alone.'

The devil offers Jesus all the kingdoms of the world, if he will pay homage to him. Jesus refuses.

The devil took Jesus to the parapet of a temple and told him to throw himself off, so that the Lord would send angels to save him. Jesus said: 'You are not to put the Lord your God to the test.'

Recipe for pancake

Flour   Eggs
Cooking oil   Water

Activities

- Talk about favourite things, such as food, pastimes and toys. Ask the children how they might feel having to do without them.
- Discuss giving up time to other people. How might Christian children do this?
- The children can draw pictures of ways in which time could be given up to help other people.

Developments

- Ask a Christian person to explain the significance of Lent for Christians.
- Visit a local church during Lent and see how the church is prepared.
- Make pancakes to remember Shrove Tuesday.
- Declare a day when the children donate to charity the money that they spend on sweets. Talk about the people who are hungry.
- Create a wall display showing the temptations of Jesus.
- Discuss the symbolism of putting ash on the forehead as a sign of repentance and humility.

Lent

During Lent Christians often give up some luxuries.
The most precious thing anyone can give up is time.

● In the four pictures, children are giving up their time.
Write down what they are doing in the spaces.

Easter –   Ideas Page

Aims

- To introduce the children to the story of Easter using the 'Stations of the Cross' which recall the final hours of Jesus' life.
- To understand the significance of the story for Christians.

1.
2.

Background

A main feature of Easter is the retelling of the story of the last days in Jesus' life. In Jerusalem, Jesus was tried by Pontius Pilate and condemned to death. He was taken outside the city and crucified. Joseph of Arimathaea took away his body for burial. In Roman Catholic and Anglo-Catholic churches there may be a series of pictures around the walls depicting the story of Good Friday. These pictures help to remind Christians of the suffering, death and self-sacrifice of Jesus. In Jerusalem, on any Friday, there are pilgrims tracing the final journey of Jesus to the crucifixion. The 14 events are pointed out to them along the way. The story of Jesus' crucifixion can be found in the New Testament, Matthew 27, Mark 15, Luke 23 and John 19.

6.
11.
13.
14.

Starting points

- Ask the children what they know about the death of Jesus.
- Talk about Easter and how it is celebrated by Christians.
- Talk about things we use to remind us of events or special times, for example a diary or photographs.

Activities

- Remind the children that in the past many people could not read. Churches often had pictures to help people remember important stories.
- Read or tell the story of the crucifixion from the New Testament.
- Ask the children either to cut the pictures up and put in order or match the picture to the corresponding text.
- The children can think of their own pictures for the other events.

How Christians celebrate Easter

1. By attending special Easter Church Services.
2. By eating Easter Eggs, Bunnies and Hot Cross Buns.
3. By stopping work.

Developments

- Talk about why it is important to Christians to remember the Easter story.
- Talk about the feelings of the people who knew Jesus. How would they have felt when he died?
- Ask the children to find the Bible references of the 14 events. Are there some they cannot find? Where might these events have come from?
- Discuss the following questions with them. What is self-sacrifice? What things would we give up? What things hurt us? How do we hurt others?
- Find out about the ways in which Christians celebrate Easter.

The Stations of the Cross

● All 14 Stations of the Cross have labels, but only six have pictures.
  Link up the correct station with its label.

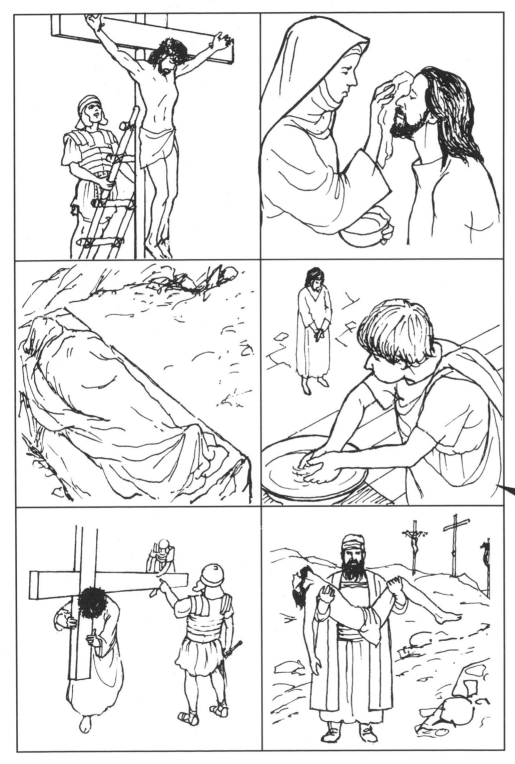

1. At Jesus' trial, he is condemned to death. Pilate washes his hands.
2. Jesus is given the cross.
3. Jesus stumbles and falls beneath the weight of the cross.
4. Jesus meets his mother Mary.
5. Simon of Cyrene is chosen to carry the cross.
6. Jesus' face is wiped by Veronica.
7. Jesus falls for a second time.
8. Jesus addresses the women of Jerusalem.
9. Jesus falls for a third time.
10. Jesus is stripped of his clothes.
11. Jesus is nailed to the cross.
12. Mary and John at the foot of the cross. Jesus dies.
13. Jesus is taken from the cross.
14. Jesus is buried in the tomb by Joseph of Arimathaea.

● Turn over and draw two other Stations of the Cross.

Aims

- To explore the symbolism of Pentecost.
- To understand its significance for Christians. The main focus is on the notion of power, in terms of the power of the Holy Spirit in the world.

Background

Pentecost comes seven weeks after Easter and is the celebration of the birth of the church. It is also called Whitsuntide and Whit Sunday because Christians long ago would be baptised in white at this time.

The story of Pentecost in Acts 2 describes the coming of the Holy Spirit among the disciples. The events took place during the Jewish festival of Pentecost, hence its name. There are many interpretations due to the strange events that took place. The followers of Jesus were feeling distraught over the death of Jesus. As they sat together, they were suddenly filled with the Holy Spirit. The notion of God's Spirit is a common feature in Old Testament tradition. The Spirit represents the power of God and several symbols or signs of it are recorded, in an attempt to explain the inexplicable events. Symbols of fire (such as flames emanating from the disciples' heads), wind and water are often used.

Starting points

- Read or tell the story of Pentecost (in Acts 2) to the children.
- Talk about the death of Jesus and how the disciples were feeling lost and sad because their teacher had gone.

How the disciples felt after Jesus' death.

1. Sadness to have lost a friend.
2. Confused to have lost their leader.
3. Determined to carry out His wishes.

Activities

- After reading the story of the Pentecost to the children, talk about the disciples' feelings after Jesus' death and how they changed from sorrow and despair to joy.
- Ask them about their experience of the power of wind and fire.
- Christians believe that when they are filled with the Holy Spirit they are filled with God's power. Discuss how Christians might show God's power in their lives.
- Ask the children to describe some of the ways this power can be shown.

POWER

Developments

- The children could paint pictures in red and white to show the wind and fire symbolising the Holy Spirit. They could cut out pictures of objects showing power and make a montage.
- Visit a church during Pentecost, to see how Christians celebrate the event.

Pentecost

- Describe the power of wind. Write down your ideas inside the kite.

- Describe the power of fire. Write down your answers inside the fire.

NOW

- The power of God gives Christians the strength to do things. Describe some things they might do.

Glossary

Advent – literally 'Coming', a period of preparation for Christmas.

Altar – the table used for the Eucharist.

Ascension – 40 days after the Resurrection, when Jesus ascended into heaven.

Ash Wednesday – first day of Lent. Some Christians have their foreheads marked with ash as a sign of repentance.

Baptism – a rite of initiation involving cleansing with water.

Catholic – has two meanings: (1.) literally 'universal'; (2.) a shortened version of Roman Catholic, a major branch of Christianity.

Christ – literally 'the anointed one', a Greek title for Jesus.

Christmas – a festival celebrating the birth of Jesus.

Church – has three meanings: (1.) the whole community of Christians; (2.) a building for worship; (3.) one denomination of Christianity (for example, the Anglican church).

Creed – a summary of beliefs.

Crucifixion – Roman method of executing criminals by nailing them to a cross.

Easter – a festival celebrating the resurrection of Jesus.

Eucharist – 'thanksgiving' meal recalling sacrificial death of Jesus.

Font – a receptacle to hold water for baptism.

Good Friday – a day commemorating the death of Jesus.

Gospel – has two meanings: (1.) 'good news' (of salvation of mankind through Jesus' death); (2.) an account of Jesus' life.

Heaven – a place or state of being united with God.

Holy Communion – a service recalling the last meal and the death of Jesus.

Icon – a picture of Jesus or the saints, an aid to worship.

Incarnation – the doctrine that God became flesh in Jesus Christ.

Jesus Christ – the central figure of Christianity.

Lectern – a stand supporting the Bible.

Lent – a season of penitence, 40 days leading up to Easter.

Mass – a term for Eucharist, often used in the Roman Catholic church.

New Testament – a collection of 27 books forming part of Christian scripture.

Old Testament – a collection of 39 books forming part of Christian scripture, shared as a basis for belief with Judaism.

Orthodox – the eastern Christian church, including Greek and Slavic, led by the Patriarchate of Constantinople.

Pentecost – a Jewish festival occuring seven weeks after the Passover. On the day of the feast, the disciples of Jesus received the Holy Spirit. Also known as Whitsun by Christians.

Pulpit – an elevated platform from which sermons are preached.

Resurrection – has three meanings: (1.) the rising from the dead of Jesus on the third day after crucifixion; (2.) the rising from the dead of believers on Judgement Day; (3.) the new risen life of Christians.

Sin – an act of rebellion against God.